Have No Fear, Snoopy!

**Selected cartoons from
YOU'RE ON THE
WRONG FOOT AGAIN,
CHARLIE BROWN**

Charles M. Schulz

CORONET BOOKS
Hodder and Stoughton

PEANUTS comic strips by Charles M. Schulz

Copyright © 1988 by United Feature Syndicate, Inc.

First published in the United States of America by Ballantine Books in 1989

Coronet edition 1990

This book comprises selected cartoons from YOU'RE ON THE WRONG FOOT AGAIN, CHARLIE BROWN and is reprinted by arrangement with Pharos Books.

British Library C.I.P.

Schulz, Charles M. (Charles Monroe), 1922–
    Have no fear, Snoopy! : selected cartoons from You're on the wrong foot again, Charlie Brown.
    1. American humorous strip cartoons – Collections from individual artists
    I. Title
    741.5'973

ISBN 0 340 51574 0

Printed and bound in Great Britain for Hodder and Stoughton Paperbacks, a division of Hodder and Stoughton Ltd., Mill Road, Dunton Green, Sevenoaks, Kent TN13 2YA.
(Editorial Office: 47 Bedford Square, London WC1B 3DP) by
Cox & Wyman Ltd., Reading.

Have No Fear, SNOOPY!

HERE, A LETTER FROM SPIKE..
Dear Snoopy,
I think I have found a new way to make some money.
8-10
Wish me luck.
your brother,
Spike
AUTHENTIC WESTERN ART
SCHULZ

PEANUTS

featuring "Good ol' Charlie Brown"

by Schulz

8-11

"I used to think you were a great engineer," she said.

8-14

"Once, I even loved you..."

"But you've gotten too big for your bridges."

SCHULZ

HERE'S THE WORLD FAMOUS EXPLORER LEADING HIS TEAM OF DIVERS TO AN UNDERWATER EXPEDITION...

STAY RIGHT WHERE YOU ARE!! FORGET IT!

LAST YEAR WHEN I WENT TO SCHOOL, I WAS IN THE WRONG ROOM FOR TWO WEEKS

THEN I GOT IN THE RIGHT ROOM, AND SAT IN THE WRONG DESK..I DIDN'T GET MY LOCKER OPEN THE WHOLE YEAR...

I WAS IN THE BAND FOR THREE DAYS BEFORE I DISCOVERED OUR SCHOOL DOESN'T HAVE A BAND!

I THINK I'LL SIGN UP FOR STAYING HOME..

8-22

PEANUTS

featuring

"Good ol' Charlie Brown"

by SCHULZ

8-25

MARCIE, WHAT WERE THE NAMES OF THOSE BOOKS THE TEACHER WANTED US TO READ THIS SUMMER?

YOU MEAN YOU HAVEN'T READ THEM YET, SIR? SCHOOL STARTS TOMORROW

I HAVE A GOOD EXCUSE..

THE LIBRARY IS CLOSED TODAY!

9-2

HEY, CHUCK, I HEARD THEM TALKING ABOUT YOU AT SCHOOL YESTERDAY...

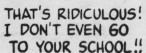

THE COMPUTER SAID YOU WERE SUPPOSED TO BE ON OUR SCHOOL BUS...

THAT'S RIDICULOUS! I DON'T EVEN GO TO YOUR SCHOOL!!

WHAT ARE YOU, CHUCK, SOME KIND OF TROUBLEMAKER?

9-7

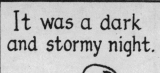

PEANUTS

featuring

"Good ol' Charlie Brown"

by SCHULZ

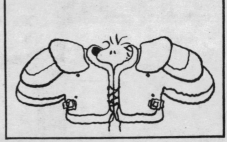

I'LL COME RUNNING DOWN THE FIELD, AND YOU TRY TO TACKLE ME...

: SIGH :

9-24

SHE'S ASLEEP MA'AM..

MAYBE WE ALL SHOULD JUST TIPTOE OUT OF THE ROOM, AND LET HER REST, OKAY?

THAT'S ALL RIGHT... IT WAS ONLY A SUGGESTION..

SCHULZ

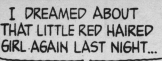

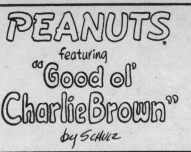

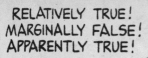

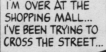

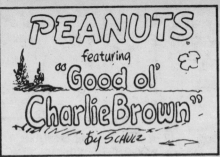

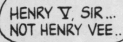

IN 1927, CHARLES LINDBERGH MADE THE FIRST NONSTOP SOLO FLIGHT FROM NEW YORK TO PARIS..

HE WAS KNOWN AS "THE LONE EAGLE"

WHO ELSE DO YOU THINK COULD HAVE MADE A FLIGHT LIKE THAT?

"THE LONE BEAGLE"

10-21

HERE'S THE "LONE BEAGLE" MAKING HIS HISTORIC FLIGHT ACROSS THE ATLANTIC TO PARIS...

10-22

FAR BELOW HE CAN SEE THE DARK WATERS OF THE ATLANTIC...

YOUR WATER DISH IS GETTING LOW..I THINK I'D BETTER FILL IT...

THE DARK WATERS OF THE ATLANTIC DISAPPEAR BENEATH HIS PLANE...

HERE'S THE "LONE BEAGLE" BACK HOME AFTER HIS HISTORIC FLIGHT FROM NEW YORK TO PARIS...

RIDING THROUGH THE CITY, HE IS GREETED BY CHEERING THRONGS IN A HUGE TICKER TAPE PARADE...

10-25

A ONE TICKER TAPE PARADE..

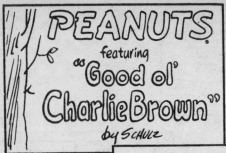

GOOD MORNING, SIR.. MY NAME IS LINUS VAN PELT... HALLOWEEN WILL SOON BE HERE, AND I'D LIKE TO TELL YOU A LITTLE ABOUT THE "GREAT PUMPKIN"

PUMPKINS? NO, WE AIN'T BOUGHT ANY PUMPKINS YET..

WELL, WHAT I REALLY MEANT WAS..

HEY, ESTELLE, ARE WE GONNA BUY ANY PUMPKINS THIS YEAR? YEAH, HALLOWEEN IS COMIN'!

10-27

I MISSED SCHOOL YESTERDAY BECAUSE I HAD A COLD...

THERE MUST BE SOMETHING GOING AROUND.. LOTS OF KIDS HAVE BEEN GETTING COLDS...

10-28

MINE WAS A LOT WORSE, THOUGH...

WHY?

BECAUSE IT HAPPENED TO ME!

MY GRAMPA IS A "FREQUENT FLIER" SO YESTERDAY HE WENT TO THE AIRPORT...

THE LADY BEHIND THE TICKET COUNTER SAID, "OH, YOU'VE ALREADY FLOWN A HUNDRED THOUSAND MILES"

"YOU DON'T HAVE TO MAKE THIS TRIP," SHE SAID.."YOU CAN GO HOME!" SO HE WENT HOME!

YOUR WHOLE FAMILY'S WEIRD, MARCIE..

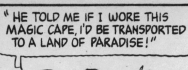

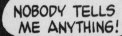

PEANUTS

featuring
"Good ol' Charlie Brown"
by SCHULZ

His bus left at midnite.

THAT'S NOT HOW YOU SPELL "MIDNIGHT"

AH, YOU RECOGNIZED THE WORD, THOUGH, DIDN'T YOU?

TODAY IS VETERANS DAY.. I ALWAYS GET TOGETHER WITH OL' BILL MAULDIN ON VETERANS DAY, AND QUAFF A FEW ROOT BEERS...

OL' BILL AND I CAN REALLY PUT 'EM AWAY..

HEY, BILL, AS LONG AS YOU'RE UP, ORDER A COUPLE MORE! I'M PAYIN'!

BUT TELL 'IM WE WANT MORE ICE CREAM IN THE NEXT ONES!

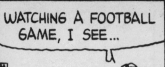